The Crater

by Mark Falstein
illustrated by Steven Francis

Chapters

Harcourt

Orlando   Boston   Dallas   Chicago   San Diego

Visit *The Learning Site!*

www.harcourtschool.com

The Crash

I'm alive. That was Soto's first thought after the crash. He could see the orange glow of the Titan sky. He could hear the *Landcraft 3*'s computer giving a report on the craft's systems.

It was a discouraging report. Forward motion, failed. Lift, failed. Communication, failed. Life support, failing fast. Soto was alive, but his landcraft was dead.

The dust storm had struck suddenly. Before Soto could react, the landcraft had been thrown out of control. He remembered the last thing he had seen. It was a crater, a huge cavity in the rocky surface of Titan. His wrecked landcraft now lay at the bottom of that crater.

Soto checked his space suit. It was not damaged as far as he could tell. He climbed out of the landcraft and inflated his portable habitat. Only after he was inside the habitat did he remove his helmet and begin to consider his problem.

He was in a crater on Titan, the largest moon of Saturn. Saturn had at least seventeen other, smaller moons and many small satellites. Titan was huge, bigger than the planet Mercury. The rest of the astronauts in Soto's group were living at Titan Base. Every day they made trips out from the base to explore Titan.

This crater was in a remote area, far from the base. Soto had been on a course toward the Great Southern Sea, near the largest of Titan's mysterious "warm spots."

Soto knew people from the base would come looking for him. But where would they look? The storm had blown him off course. How far off course? Where was he?

He looked at the shadows. Even through thick clouds, the sun shone brightly, causing dark shadows. Giant Saturn, only 1.2 million kilometers away, also gave off light that was reflected from the sun.

The orange-colored clouds kept Soto from seeing Saturn's wide rings of rocks, gas, and ice. Still, he knew they were up there.

Stuck!

The cavity of the crater had steep walls. The crater had probably been created when a meteor hit Titan's surface centuries ago. Soto's wrecked landcraft was in deep shadow. A rescue party might not spot him or the ship.

He wanted to call the base on his radio, but radio signals did not work well on Titan. There was too much interference from Saturn. Saturn's magnetic fields made it difficult to send messages between the landcrafts and the base.

He had to get out of the crater.

Soto ate and rested. He could carry the habitat, but food would be a problem if he were not rescued soon. He had only enough food for two days.

He gazed at the crater's high wall. The view was discouraging. He had climbed steeper rocks on Earth, and at Titan's low gravity he weighed only a fraction of his normal weight. However, Soto had been living at low gravity for two Earth years. Moving around was so easy that his muscles had become weak. Was he still strong enough to climb the crater wall?

Soto was a pioneer. He and the others on this remote moon were preparing the way for a migration. Titan Base would be the foundation for a domed city.

Hydrogen was the reason for the migration. It was 2064, and Earth now ran on hydrogen fusion power. It took the new fusion spaceships just months to reach Saturn and only weeks to reach Mars. Saturn was essentially a giant hydrogen mine that would never run out.

Still, there were other reasons to be here. Ever since the Cassini and Huygens probes of 2004, scientists had wanted to learn more about Titan's warm spots.

Titan was a world of rock and ice. The surface temperature was about -180°C. Yet here and there were areas no colder than a winter day on Earth. What were they? Where did this heat come from?

Soto began the climb. In some places he had to pull himself up hand over hand. In others he had to leap over deep, wide cracks.

It would soon be night. He had to set up the habitat. It would be dangerous to...

Discovery

Soto stopped. He checked his space suit's built-in computer. Yes! *Right here* was a warm spot. It was almost warm enough to take off his space suit—if Titan had had any oxygen to breathe. But Soto knew better than that. Titan's atmosphere was mostly nitrogen.

He glanced around. What were those dark streaks running along the rock? They looked like orange moss.

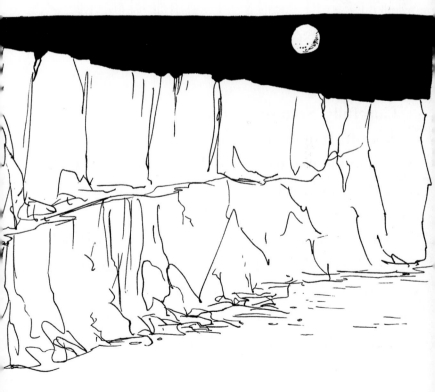

Carefully, Soto scraped up some of the soft, dark stuff. It came away from the rock with difficulty. He looked around and found a large, flat rock that could serve as a foundation for his portable habitat.

After setting up the habitat, Soto kept his helmet on inside, in case the moss was dangerous in some way. He set up the portable lab to test the substance. It was alive! Not only alive, but edible. Not only edible, but nourishing! It was a living, growing plant.

No, it wasn't a plant. Plants grew only on Earth. This was something else, but it was alive. His computer told him that the moss was organized in cells. It contained the same elements as life on Earth. If he ate it, his body could break it down for his own cells to use. To a scientist, that was what *nourishing* meant.

Still Soto didn't eat it. The computer did not indicate any poisons, but why should he experiment on himself? He wasn't starving—yet.

On Earth he would have observed whether or not animals ate the moss. That would tell him whether it were safe. But there were no animals on Titan—or were there?

The Oxygen Mystery

Soto slept. The next morning he gathered more of the Titan "moss."

He knew that all living things depend on oxygen. He wondered where the oxygen in this living thing could have come from. Soto remembered that way back in 1998, a satellite from the European Space Agency had passed near Titan. It had sent back to Earth evidence of water vapor in Titan's atmosphere.

Plants on Earth could adapt to different conditions. Maybe there was enough oxygen in the air for a "plant" to adapt to the conditions on Titan.

Then Soto considered that Titan had plenty of water in the form of ice. Living things deep in Earth's oceans got oxygen directly from water. Maybe life here had a way of taking it from ice.

He studied the moss closely. He couldn't wait to get back to the base so he could analyze it in a bigger lab.

If only someone would rescue him...

Late on the second day, Soto reached the rim of the crater and climbed out. He was very hungry.

He ate some of the Titan moss.

It tasted…*brown*. It was not something he would choose to eat, but it was edible.

The moss kept Soto alive for four days.

On the fifth day after leaving the crater, Soto spotted a landcraft flying in the distance. He burst into laughter as the silver craft streaked across the sky.

Soto waved and waved. Then he tried his radio. Since the landcraft was so close, the radio worked.

"Soto?" a familiar voice asked. "Is that really you down there?"

"It sure is!" he shouted into his radio. "Come and get me!"

After the ship landed, Soto did not waste any time getting aboard. He had never been so glad to see another human being.

"You're looking very fit for someone who's been missing for almost a week," his friend Beltran said. "What have you been living on—rocks?"

Soto smiled. There was a lot to tell, but he would have to make an official report first.

"Let me just say this for now," Soto said. "If our food supply at Titan Base ever fails, we won't starve."